SUPER SECRET C·O·D·E·S & JOKES

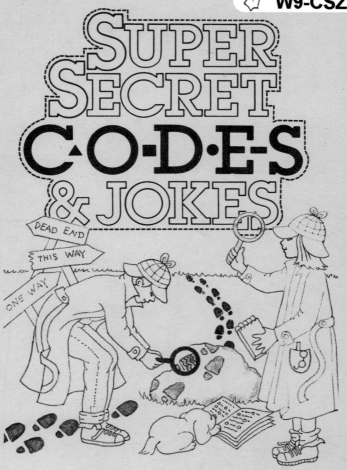

kidsbooks Incorporated

Copyright © 1990 Tony John and Kidsbooks Inc.

7004 N. California Ave.
Chicago, Illinois 60645

CODE CHART #1

A	B	C	D	E	F	G
10	21	16	30	35	24	18

H	I	J	K	L	M	N
27	32	12	34	22	14	13

O	P	Q	R	S	T	U
20	28	26	11	29	31	15

V	W	X	Y	Z
33	25	17	23	19

WHY ARE PIGS SUCH GREAT SPORTS FANS?

$\overline{21}\ \overline{35}\ \overline{16}\ \overline{10}\ \overline{15}\ \overline{29}\ \overline{35}$

$\overline{31}\ \overline{27}\ \overline{35}\ \overline{23}$ ' $\overline{11}\ \overline{35}$

$\overline{10}\ \overline{22}\ \overline{25}\ \overline{10}\ \overline{23}\ \overline{29}$

$\overline{11}\ \overline{20}\ \overline{20}\ \overline{31}\ \overline{32}\ \overline{13}\ \overline{18}$!

"WHY DON'T YOU CONVINCE
YOUR BROTHER THAT HE'S
NOT A CHICKEN?"

" $\overline{21}\ \overline{35}\ \overline{16}\ \overline{10}\ \overline{15}\ \overline{29}\ \overline{35}$

$\overline{32}$ $\overline{16}\ \overline{10}\ \overline{13}$

$\overline{15}\ \overline{29}\ \overline{35}$ $\overline{31}\ \overline{27}\ \overline{35}$

$\overline{35}\ \overline{18}\ \overline{18}\ \overline{29}$!"

SOLUTIONS CAN BE FOUND
IN THE BACK OF THIS BOOK.

CODE CHART #2

real letter:	A	B	C	D	E	F	G
code letter:	LM	DD	HI	RS	ZZ	YZ	KL

real letter:	H	I	J	K	L	M	N
code letter:	ST	NO	UV	PQ	XY	FG	WX

real letter:	O	P	Q	R	S	T	U
code letter:	EE	AA	GH	TU	VW	AZ	BB

real letter:	V	W	X	Y	Z
code letter:	OP	JK	CC	MN	QR

WHAT DOG KEEPS THE BEST TIME?

$\overline{\text{LM}}$ $\overline{\text{JK}}$ $\overline{\text{LM}}$ $\overline{\text{AZ}}$ $\overline{\text{HI}}$ $\overline{\text{ST}}$

$\overline{\text{RS}}$ $\overline{\text{EE}}$ $\overline{\text{KL}}$!

"WHAT'S THE CHANCE OF
BORROWING FIVE DOLLARS FROM YOU?"

" $\overline{\text{VW}}$ $\overline{\text{XY}}$ $\overline{\text{NO}}$ $\overline{\text{FG}}$ $\overline{\text{LM}}$ $\overline{\text{WX}}$ $\overline{\text{RS}}$

$\overline{\text{WX}}$ $\overline{\text{EE}}$ $\overline{\text{WX}}$ $\overline{\text{EE}}$ ' $\overline{\text{LM}}$ $\overline{\text{WX}}$ $\overline{\text{RS}}$

$\overline{\text{VW}}$ $\overline{\text{XY}}$ $\overline{\text{NO}}$ $\overline{\text{FG}}$ $\overline{\text{NO}}$ $\overline{\text{VW}}$

$\overline{\text{EE}}$ $\overline{\text{BB}}$ $\overline{\text{AZ}}$ $\overline{\text{EE}}$ $\overline{\text{YZ}}$

$\overline{\text{AZ}}$ $\overline{\text{EE}}$ $\overline{\text{JK}}$ $\overline{\text{WX}}$!"

WHY DO HAMBURGERS MAKE GOOD
BASEBALL PLAYERS?

$\overline{\text{AZ}}$ $\overline{\text{ST}}$ $\overline{\text{ZZ}}$ $\overline{\text{MN}}$ ' $\overline{\text{TU}}$ $\overline{\text{ZZ}}$

$\overline{\text{KL}}$ $\overline{\text{TU}}$ $\overline{\text{ZZ}}$ $\overline{\text{LM}}$ $\overline{\text{AZ}}$ $\overline{\text{LM}}$ $\overline{\text{AZ}}$

$\overline{\text{AZ}}$ $\overline{\text{ST}}$ $\overline{\text{ZZ}}$ $\overline{\text{AA}}$ $\overline{\text{XY}}$ $\overline{\text{LM}}$ $\overline{\text{AZ}}$ $\overline{\text{ZZ}}$!

CODE CHART #3

A	B	C	D	E	F	G	H
+	++	+++	−	−−	−−−	½	½½

I	J	K	L	M	N
½½½	¼	¼¼	¼¼¼	=	==

O	P	Q	R	S	T	U	V
===	+−	−+	½¼	¼½	+½	½+	−½

W	X	Y	Z
½++	−¼	¼−	+−½

½++ ½½ −− ==   ½½½ ¼½   +

½¼ ½½½ −½ −− ½¼   ¼¼¼ ½½½ ¼¼ −−

+½ ½½ −−   ¼¼¼ −− +½ +½ −− ½¼

" +½ " ?

½++ ½½ −− ==

½½½ +½   = ½+ ¼½ +½

++ −−

+++ ½¼ === ¼½ ¼½ −− − !

"WHY DID YOU STOP TAKING SINGING LESSONS?"

"
____   ____
=   ¼ -

____   ___   ____   _____ ____   ___   ____
+½   --   +   +++   ½½   --   ½¼

____   _____   _____   ____
+½   ===   ¼¼¼   -

____   ____   _____
=   --   ½½½

_____   ____   ____
½++   +   ¼½

____   ___   ___   ____   ____   ___   ____
+½   ½½   ½¼   ===   ½++   ½½½   ==   ½

____   ___   ____
+½   ½½   --

____   _____   ____   ____   _____
+-   ½½½   +   ==   ===

_____   ____   ____   !"
===   ---   ---

WHAT QUESTION CAN NEVER BE ANSWERED BY "YES"?

____   ___   ____   _____   ____   ____
+   ½¼   --   ¼-   ===   ½+

____   ___   _____   ____   ____   ____   ?
+   ¼½   ¼¼¼   --   --   +-

WHAT WAS THE RABBIT DOING IN FRONT OF THE CANDLE?

"ARE YOU AFRAID OF HEIGHTS?"

WHY DO WE BUY CLOTHES?

CODE CHART #5

	A	B	C	D	E	F	G
A	D	E	L	M	T	U	Y
B	C	F	K	N	S	V	Z
C	B	G	J	O	R	W	
D	A	H	I	P	Q	X	

example: BD=N

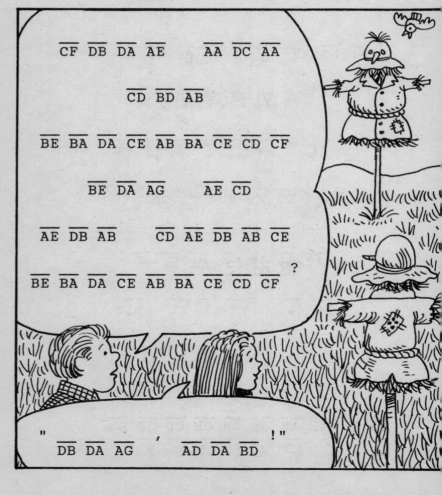

WHAT KIND OF SHOES ARE MADE OUT OF BANANA SKINS?

‾‾ ‾‾ ‾‾ ‾‾ ‾‾ ‾‾ ‾‾ ‾‾ !
BE AC DC DD DD AB CE BE

WHAT MOST RESEMBLES HALF A CHEESE?

‾‾ ‾‾ ‾‾   ‾‾ ‾‾ ‾‾ ‾‾ ‾‾
AE DB AB   CD AE DB AB CE

‾‾ ‾‾ ‾‾ ‾‾ !
DB DA AC BB

WHAT BECOMES HIGHER WHEN THE HEAD IS OFF?

‾‾   ‾‾ ‾‾ ‾‾ ‾‾ ‾‾ ‾‾ !
DA   DD DC AC AC CD CF

WHAT ROOM CAN NO ONE ENTER?

‾‾   ‾‾ ‾‾ ‾‾ ‾‾ ‾‾ ‾‾ ‾‾ ‾‾ !
DA   AD AF BE DB CE CD CD AD

CODE CHART #6

A=⊙ N=□

B=⊡ O=□□

C=● P=○

D=⊙⊙ Q=○○

E=⊡⊡ R=□○

F=●● S=○□

G=⊙⊡ T=□○□

H=□⊙ U=○□○

I=⊙□⊙ V=⊡⊡

J=⊡⊙⊡ W=⊡□

K=■■ X=○⊙

L=□● Y=⊙○

M=●⊡ Z=⊙□⊙

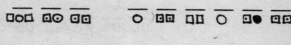

WHAT KIND OF BRICK IS SOFT?

__ __ __ __ __ __ __ ?

WHY CAN'T YOU TRUST BANK CLERKS WITH SECRETS?

__ __ __ __ __ __ __ __ __

__ __ __ __ ' __ __

__ __ __ __ __ __ __ __ !

WHAT DO YOU ALWAYS FIND IN YOUR POCKET WHEN YOU REACH IN?

__ __ __ __ __ __ __ !

CODE CHART #7

A= 275 N= 175
B= 475 O= 425
C= 125 P= 350
D= 525 Q= 250
E= 725 R= 625
F= 325 S= 100
G= 500 T= 550
H= 675 U= 450
I= 225 V= 700
J= 650 W= 300
K= 600 X= 575
L= 150 Y= 375
M= 400 Z= 200

675 425 300

300 425 450 150 525

375 425 450

500 625 725 725 550

100 400 425 600 725 375

550 675 725

475 725 275 625   ?

300 225 550 675   275

475 725 275 625   675 450 500 !

WHAT GOOD IS HAVING A
MICROWAVE FIREPLACE?

375 425 450   125 275 175

100 350 725 175 525

275 175

725 700 725 175 225 175 500

225 175

325 625 425 175 550

425 325   550 675 725

325 225 625 725   225 175

450 175 525 725 625

725 225 500 675 550

400 225 175 450 550 725 100 !

CODE CHART #8

real letter	A	B	C	D	E	F	G	H	I	J	K	L	M
code letter	J	F	L	G	N	P	R	T	W	A	Q	Y	U

real letter	N	O	P	Q	R	S	T	U	V	W	X	Y	Z
code letter	B	V	H	C	M	X	I	D	O	S	E	Z	K

"DO YOU THINK WE OUGHT TO HAVE
BUTTERFLY CHAIRS?"

" B̄ V̄ !   Ȳ N̄ Ī   Ī T̄ N̄ Ū

P̄ Ȳ Z̄   J̄ M̄ V̄ D̄ B̄ Ḡ ! "

WHAT DO THEY DO WITH THE
LEFTOVER HOLES IN DOUGHNUTS?

Ī T̄ N̄ Z̄   Ī W̄ N̄   Ī T̄ N̄ Ū

D̄ H̄   S̄ W̄ Ī T̄

X̄ Ī M̄ W̄ B̄ R̄   J̄ B̄ Ḡ

Ū J̄ Q̄ N̄   P̄ W̄ X̄ T̄

B̄ N̄ Ī X̄ !

"YOU HAVE YOUR SHOES ON
THE WRONG FEET!"

" Ī T̄ N̄ Z̄ ' M̄ N̄   Ī T̄ N̄

V̄ B̄ Ȳ Z̄   P̄ N̄ N̄ Ī

W̄   T̄ J̄ Ō N̄ ! "

	1	2	3	4	5	6	7
■	V	W	X	Y	Z		
▲	O	P	Q	R	S	T	U
✱	H	I	J	K	L	M	N
●	A	B	C	D	E	F	G

"WHERE'S YOUR DOG?"

"
$\overline{✱2}$　$\overline{▲5}$ $\overline{▲2}$ $\overline{✱2}$ $\overline{✱5}$ $\overline{✱5}$ $\overline{●5}$ $\overline{●4}$

$\overline{▲5}$ $\overline{▲2}$ $\overline{▲1}$ $\overline{▲6}$

$\overline{▲4}$ $\overline{●5}$ $\overline{✱6}$ $\overline{▲1}$ $\overline{■1}$ $\overline{●5}$ $\overline{▲4}$　$\overline{▲1}$ $\overline{✱7}$

$\overline{✱1}$ $\overline{✱2}$ $\overline{✱6}$　$\overline{●1}$ $\overline{✱7}$ $\overline{●4}$

$\overline{✱7}$ $\overline{▲1}$ $\overline{■2}$　$\overline{✱1}$ $\overline{●5}$ ' $\overline{▲5}$

$\overline{●7}$ $\overline{▲1}$ $\overline{✱7}$ $\overline{●5}$!"

"MY NAME IS JOE, WHAT CAN I CALL YOU?"

"
$\overline{●1}$ $\overline{✱7}$ $\overline{■4}$ $\overline{▲6}$ $\overline{✱1}$ $\overline{✱2}$ $\overline{✱7}$ $\overline{●7}$

$\overline{■4}$ $\overline{▲1}$ $\overline{▲7}$　$\overline{■2}$ $\overline{●1}$ $\overline{✱7}$ $\overline{▲6}$ '

$\overline{✱3}$ $\overline{▲7}$ $\overline{▲5}$ $\overline{▲6}$

$\overline{●4}$ $\overline{▲1}$ $\overline{✱7}$ ' $\overline{▲6}$　$\overline{●3}$ $\overline{●1}$ $\overline{✱5}$ $\overline{✱5}$

$\overline{✱6}$ $\overline{●5}$　$\overline{✱5}$ $\overline{●1}$ $\overline{▲6}$ $\overline{●5}$

$\overline{●6}$ $\overline{▲1}$ $\overline{▲4}$

$\overline{●4}$ $\overline{✱2}$ $\overline{✱7}$ $\overline{✱7}$ $\overline{●5}$ $\overline{▲4}$!"

A= • N= •|•
B= •• O= •—•
C= ••• P= |•|
D= | Q= —•—
E= |I R= •|••
F= III S= ••|•
G= — T= |—
H= = U= —|
I= ≡ V= |=
J= •| W= =|
K= •— X= ||—
L= |• Y= —||
M= —• Z= ||=

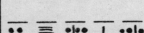

"IF YOU SHOVELED SNOW FOR 25
PEOPLE AND THEY EACH PAID
YOU FOUR DOLLARS, WHAT
WOULD YOU GET?"

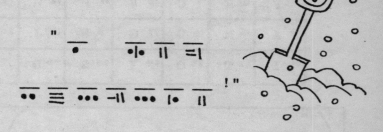

"IS THIS THE END OF THE LINE?"

WHAT IS

A BULL

CALLED

WHEN

HE'S

SLEEPING?

A

BULLDOZER!

WHAT GOES UP INTO THE AIR WHITE AND COMES DOWN YELLOW AND WHITE?

SUN	TUE		SAT	WED	WED	!
14	2		13	17	17	

WHAT DO YOU GET WHEN YOU CROSS A KANGAROO WITH A 747 JET?

SUN		THU	MON	SUN	TUE	SAT
14		11	1	14	2	13

MON	WED	SUN	MON
22	3	14	22

MON	SUN	SAT	SAT	THU
15	14	6	13	25

THU	WED	TUE	MON	MON
25	3	23	8	22

WED	TUE	THU	THU	!
3	23	11	25	

CODE CHART #12

★		■		▲		●	
1	Q	1	E	1	S	1	I
2	H	2	P	2	R	2	X
3	Y	3	L	3	B	3	O
4	M	4	G	4	T	4	D
5	C	5	U	5	F	5	W
6	J	6	K	6	N	6	Z
		7	A	7	V		

HOW DO YOU MAKE NOTES
OF STONE?

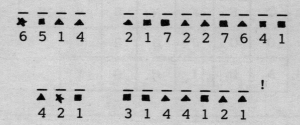

HOW CAN YOU TELL IF THIS IS
A DOGWOOD TREE?

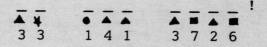

"HOW DO YOU LIKE SCHOOL?"

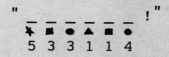

CODE CHART #13

	10	20	30	40	50	60	70
a	D	E	L	M	T	U	Y
b	C	F	K	N	S	V	Z
c	B	G	J	O	R	W	
d	A	H	I	P	Q	X	

HOW DO YOU MAKE SOUP GOLD?

$$\overline{40}\ \overline{60}\ \overline{50}\ \ \ \overline{30}\ \overline{40}$$
d   a   a   d   b

$$\overline{20}\ \overline{40}\ \overline{60}\ \overline{50}\ \overline{50}\ \overline{20}\ \overline{20}\ \overline{40}$$
b   c   a   c   a   a   a   b

$$\overline{10}\ \overline{10}\ \overline{50}\ \overline{50}\ \overline{40}\ \overline{50}\ \overline{50}\ !$$
b   d   c   c   c   a   b

WHAT'S PURPLE AND FLIES?

$$\overline{50}\ \overline{60}\ \overline{40}\ \overline{20}\ \overline{50}\ \overline{20}\ \overline{50}\ \overline{10}\ \overline{40}\ \overline{20}\ !$$
b   a   d   a   c   c   c   d   d   a

WHAT'S HIGHER THAN A BUILDING AND SEEMS SMALLER THAN A FROG?

$$\overline{10}\ \ \ \ \overline{50}\ \overline{50}\ \overline{10}\ \overline{50}\ !$$
d   b   a   d   c

CODE CHART #14

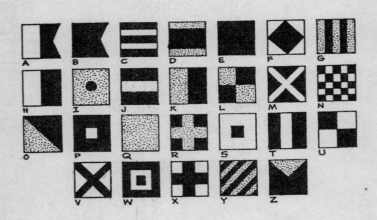

"DID YOU HEAR THE STORY ABOUT THE MOUNTAIN?"

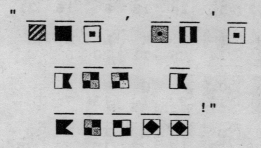

WHAT DOES A VAMPIRE DO WHEN HE GETS TIRED OF WORKING?

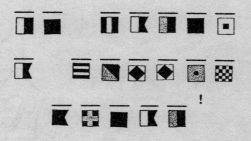

WHAT KIND OF SANDWICHES DO SAILORS LIKE?

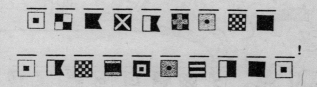

CODE CHART #15

A	B	C	D	E	F	G
12	5	24	18	8	16	21

H	I	J	K	L	M	N
2	14	26	11	20	6	4

	O	P	Q	R	S	
	17	9	1	13	7	

T	U	V	W	X	Y	Z
23	19	10	22	15	3	25

WHAT DO YOU CALL A GIANT
BELL THAT'S COVERED WITH HAIR?

$\overline{11}$ $\overline{14}$ $\overline{4}$ $\overline{21}$ $\overline{21}$ $\overline{17}$ $\overline{4}$ $\overline{21}$!

WHERE'S A GOOD PLACE TO GO
WHEN YOU'RE BROKE?

$\overline{23}$ $\overline{17}$ $\overline{22}$ $\overline{17}$ $\overline{13}$ $\overline{11}$!

WHAT PEN SHOULD NEVER BE USED
FOR WRITING?

$\overline{12}$ $\overline{9}$ $\overline{14}$ $\overline{21}$ $\overline{9}$ $\overline{8}$ $\overline{4}$!

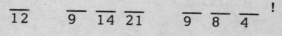

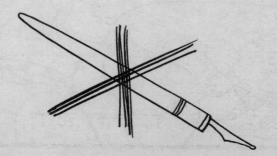

CODE CHART #16

real letter	A	B	C	D	E	F	G
code letter	L	H	Q	V	Z	D	N

real letter	H	I	J	K	L	M	N
code letter	S	E	P	A	R	I	Y

real letter	O	P	Q	R	S	T	U
code letter	M	B	J	U	G	O	X

real letter	V	W	X	Y	Z
code letter	F	T	K	W	C

WHAT COMES WITH AN AIRPLANE,
GOES WITH AN AIRPLANE AND IS
NO USE TO AN AIRPLANE?

$\overline{Y}\ \overline{M}\ \overline{E}\ \overline{G}\ \overline{Z}$!

WHO GETS PAID FOR NEVER DOING
A DAY'S WORK?

$\overline{L}$ $\overline{Y}\ \overline{E}\ \overline{N}\ \overline{S}\ \overline{O}$

$\overline{T}\ \overline{L}\ \overline{O}\ \overline{Q}\ \overline{S}\ \overline{I}\ \overline{L}\ \overline{Y}$!

WHAT GOES UP AND NEVER
GOES DOWN?

$\overline{W}\ \overline{M}\ \overline{X}\ \overline{U}$ $\overline{L}\ \overline{N}\ \overline{Z}$!

CODE CHART #17

A	B	C	D	E	F
35	85	20	90	105	50

G	H	I	J	K	L
45	70	115	5	110	10

M	N	O	P	Q	R
60	100	80	30	75	95

S	T	U	V
25	120	55	125

W	X	Y	Z
40	15	65	130

40 70 105 95 105 25 '

35   45 80 80 90

30 10 35 20 105   50 80 95   35

45 115 35 100 120   35 30 105

120 80   25 115 120 ?

35 100 65 40 70 105 95 105

115 120   40 35 100 120 25   120 80 !

WHY DOES TARZAN SWING THROUGH THE TREES?

$\overline{25}\ \overline{80}\qquad \overline{70}\ \overline{105}$

$\overline{40}\ \overline{80}\ \overline{100}\ \text{'}\ \overline{120}\qquad \overline{45}\ \overline{105}\ \overline{120}$

$\overline{70}\ \overline{115}\ \overline{25}$

$\overline{25}\ \overline{70}\ \overline{80}\ \overline{105}\ \overline{25}$

$\overline{90}\ \overline{115}\ \overline{95}\ \overline{120}\ \overline{65}\ \text{!}$

HOW CAN YOU TELL IF AN ELEPHANT HAS BEEN IN YOUR KITCHEN?

$\overline{85}\ \overline{65}\qquad \overline{120}\ \overline{70}\ \overline{105}$

$\overline{30}\ \overline{105}\ \overline{35}\ \overline{100}\ \overline{55}\ \overline{120}$

$\overline{25}\ \overline{70}\ \overline{105}\ \overline{10}\ \overline{10}\ \overline{25}$

$\overline{115}\ \overline{100}\qquad \overline{120}\ \overline{70}\ \overline{105}$

$\overline{25}\ \overline{115}\ \overline{100}\ \overline{110}\ \text{!}$

CODE CHART #18

A	B	C	D	E	F	G
G	K	S	A	Z	J	R

H	I	J	K	L	M	N
D	V	F	M	T	U	B

O	P	Q	R	S	T	U
N	O	W	E	L	C	X

V	W	X	Y	Z
Q	H	Y	P	I

"DO YOU REALLY HAVE BAD LUCK?"

$\overline{V}\ \overline{J}$ $\overline{V}\ \overline{C}$ $\overline{L}\ \overline{C}\ \overline{G}\ \overline{E}\ \overline{C}\ \overline{Z}\ \overline{A}$

$\overline{E}\ \overline{G}\ \overline{V}\ \overline{B}\ \overline{V}\ \overline{B}\ \overline{R}$ $\overline{L}\ \overline{N}\ \overline{X}\ \overline{O}$'

$\overline{V}$'$\overline{A}$ $\overline{K}\ \overline{Z}$

$\overline{L}\ \overline{C}\ \overline{G}\ \overline{B}\ \overline{A}\ \overline{V}\ \overline{B}\ \overline{R}$ $\overline{C}\ \overline{D}\ \overline{Z}\ \overline{E}\ \overline{Z}$

$\overline{H}\ \overline{V}\ \overline{C}\ \overline{D}$

$\overline{G}$ $\overline{J}\ \overline{N}\ \overline{E}\ \overline{M}$!"

NAME A LIQUID THAT CAN'T FREEZE.

$\overline{D}\ \overline{N}\ \overline{C}$ $\overline{H}\ \overline{G}\ \overline{C}\ \overline{Z}\ \overline{E}$!

CODE CHART #19

A	B	C	D	E	F	G
12	1	13	4	15	9	14

	H	I	J	K	L	
	7	3	19	11	17	

M	N	O	P	Q	R	S
6	10	5	21	8	22	24

T	U	V	W	X	Y	Z
20	2	26	18	25	23	16

"WHY DO THEY CALL YOUR
BROTHER CHOCOLATE BAR?"

"
 $\overline{1}$ $\overline{15}$ $\overline{13}$ $\overline{12}$ $\overline{2}$ $\overline{24}$ $\overline{15}$

 $\overline{7}$ $\overline{15}$ ' $\overline{24}$

$\overline{7}$ $\overline{12}$ $\overline{17}$ $\overline{9}$ $\overline{10}$ $\overline{2}$ $\overline{20}$ $\overline{24}$!"

WHERE WERE THE FIRST
DOUGHNUTS FRIED?

$\overline{3}$ $\overline{10}$ $\overline{14}$ $\overline{22}$ $\overline{15}$ $\overline{15}$ $\overline{13}$ $\overline{15}$!

IF APRIL SHOWERS BRING MAY
FLOWERS, WHAT DO MAY FLOWERS
BRING?

$\overline{21}$ $\overline{3}$ $\overline{17}$ $\overline{14}$ $\overline{22}$ $\overline{3}$ $\overline{6}$ $\overline{24}$!

CODE CHART #20

A= 7   N= 4
B= 14 O= 13
C= 1   P= 18
D= 22 Q= 10
E= 8   R= 19
F= 15 S= 3
G= 23 T= 20
H= 9   U= 24
I= 16 V= 26
J= 2   W= 11
K= 17 X= 25
L= 6   Y= 21
M= 12 Z= 5

$\overline{11}\ \overline{9}\ \overline{7}\ \overline{20}$

$\overline{20}\ \overline{16}\ \overline{12}\ \overline{8}$

$\overline{3}\ \overline{18}\ \overline{8}\ \overline{6}\ \overline{6}\ \overline{8}\ \overline{22}$

$\overline{14}\ \overline{7}\ \overline{1}\ \overline{17}\ \overline{11}\ \overline{7}\ \overline{19}\ \overline{22}$

$\overline{7}\ \overline{4}\ \overline{22}$

$\overline{15}\ \overline{13}\ \overline{19}\ \overline{11}\ \overline{7}\ \overline{19}\ \overline{22}$

$\overline{16}\ \overline{3}\quad \overline{20}\ \overline{9}\ \overline{8}$

$\overline{3}\ \overline{7}\ \overline{12}\ \overline{8}$?

$\overline{4}\ \overline{13}\ \overline{13}\ \overline{4}$!

WHAT TRAVELS ABOUT AND WEARS
OUT SHOES, BUT HAS NO SHOES TO
WEAR?

$\overline{7}$ $\quad$ $\overline{15}$ $\overline{13}$ $\overline{13}$ $\overline{20}$ $\overline{14}$ $\overline{7}$ $\overline{6}$ $\overline{6}$!

"IF I HAD TWO HOTDOGS AND YOU
HAD TWO HOTDOGS, WHAT WOULD WE
HAVE?

" $\overline{6}$ $\overline{24}$ $\overline{4}$ $\overline{1}$ $\overline{9}$!"

"DID YOU HEAR THE JOKE ABOUT
THE BOY WHO POPPED THE
POTATO CHIP BAG?"

" $\overline{21}$ $\overline{8}$ $\overline{3}$ $\quad$ ' $\quad$ $\overline{16}$ $\overline{20}$

$\overline{11}$ $\overline{7}$ $\overline{3}$ $\quad$ $\overline{1}$ $\overline{19}$ $\overline{24}$ $\overline{12}$ $\overline{14}$ $\overline{21}$!"

CODE CHART #21

A	B	C	D	E	F
+6	4	+7	3	+1	+8

G	H	I	J	K	L
5	+2	−3	+9	−2	6

M	N	O	P	Q	R
+3	−4	−1	2	+4	−6

S	T	U	V	W	X
7	+5	1	−5	8	−7

Y	Z
9	−8

WHEN IS THE WORST WEATHER FOR RATS AND MICE?

$$\overline{}_{8} \ \overline{}_{+2} \ \overline{}_{+1} \ \overline{}_{-4} \qquad \overline{}_{-3} \ \overline{}_{+5}$$

$$\overline{}_{-6} \ \overline{}_{+6} \ \overline{}_{-3} \ \overline{}_{-4} \ \overline{}_{7} \qquad \overline{}_{+7} \ \overline{}_{+6} \ \overline{}_{+5} \ \overline{}_{7}$$

$$\overline{}_{+6} \ \overline{}_{-4} \ \overline{}_{3} \qquad \overline{}_{3} \ \overline{}_{-1} \ \overline{}_{5} \ \overline{}_{7} \ !$$

WHAT MAKES A ROAD BROAD?

$$\overline{}_{+5} \ \overline{}_{+2} \ \overline{}_{+1} \qquad \overline{}_{6} \ \overline{}_{+1} \ \overline{}_{+5} \ \overline{}_{+5} \ \overline{}_{+1} \ \overline{}_{-6}$$

$$" \ \overline{}_{4} \ " \ !$$

"IF A LION WERE STALKING YOU, WHAT STEPS WOULD YOU TAKE?"

$$" \ \overline{}_{+5} \ \overline{}_{+2} \ \overline{}_{+1}$$

$$\overline{}_{6} \ \overline{}_{-1} \ \overline{}_{-4} \ \overline{}_{5} \ \overline{}_{+1} \ \overline{}_{7} \ \overline{}_{+5}$$

$$\overline{}_{7} \ \overline{}_{+5} \ \overline{}_{+1} \ \overline{}_{2} \ \overline{}_{7} \qquad \overline{}_{-3}$$

$$\overline{}_{+7} \ \overline{}_{-1} \ \overline{}_{1} \ \overline{}_{6} \ \overline{}_{3} \ ! \ "$$

WHAT IS THE NAME OF THE
FEATHERS THAT GROW
ON A CHICKEN'S WING?

$\overline{1}$ $\overline{22}$ $\overline{24}$ $\overline{1}$ $\overline{26}$ $\overline{25}$ $\overline{20}$

$\overline{6}$ $\overline{25}$ $\overline{5}$ $\overline{19}$ $\overline{22}$ $\overline{25}$ $\overline{18}$ $\overline{7}$!

HENRY THE BUTCHER IS SIX FEET
TALL AND HAS BROWN HAIR.
WHAT DOES HE WEIGH?

$\overline{13}$ $\overline{25}$ $\overline{5}$ $\overline{19}$!

"IF I HAD A SLICE OF PIZZA
AND YOU HAD ONLY A BITE, WHAT
WOULD YOU DO?"

" $\overline{7}$ $\overline{1}$ $\overline{18}$ $\overline{5}$ $\overline{19}$ $\overline{1}$ $\overline{22}$

$\overline{24}$ $\overline{19}$!"

CODE CHART #23

A= 8B N= 1D
B= 5D O= 5E
C= 1B P= 4B
D= 6E Q= 2H
E= 4H R= 6M
F= 7I S= 5C
G= 2B T= 7F
H= 9C U= 3D
I= 8D V= 2J
J= 2G W= 6B
K= 3B X= 3K
L= 9N Y= 1G
M= 1D Z= 7C

WHAT DID THE PENCIL SAY TO THE
PAPER?

"$\overline{}$ $\overline{}$ $\overline{}$ $\overline{}$ $\overline{}$ $\overline{}$
  8D   6E 5E 7F   1D 1G

$\overline{}$ $\overline{}$ $\overline{}$ $\overline{}$ $\overline{}$ $\overline{}$
4H 1G 4H 5C   5E 1D

$\overline{}$ $\overline{}$ $\overline{}$!"
1G 5E 3D

"DOES THE WATER ALWAYS COME
THROUGH THE ROOF OF YOUR CAR?"

"$\overline{}$ $\overline{}$ $\overline{}$ $\overline{}$ $\overline{}$ $\overline{}$ $\overline{}$ $\overline{}$
  5E 1D 9N 1G   6B 9C 4H 1D

$\overline{}$ $\overline{}$ $\overline{}$ $\overline{}$ $\overline{}$ $\overline{}$ $\overline{}$!"
8D 7F   6M 8B 8D 1D 5C

WHAT DID ONE POTATO CHIP SAY
TO THE OTHER?

"$\overline{}$ $\overline{}$ $\overline{}$' $\overline{}$ $\overline{}$ $\overline{}$
  9N 4H 7F   5C   2B 5E

$\overline{}$ $\overline{}$ $\overline{}$
7I 5E 6M

$\overline{}$ $\overline{}$ $\overline{}$ $\overline{}$."
8B   6E 8D 4B

CODE CHART #24

	A	B	C	D	E	F	G	H	I
1	C	D	I	J	O	P	U	V	
2	B	E	H	K	N	Q	T	W	Z
3	A	F	G	L	M	R	S	X	Y

$\overline{2H}$ $\overline{2C}$ $\overline{3A}$ $\overline{2G}$ $\overline{1B}$ $\overline{1C}$ $\overline{1B}$

$\overline{2G}$ $\overline{2C}$ $\overline{2B}$

$\overline{2C}$ $\overline{1E}$ $\overline{3F}$ $\overline{3G}$ $\overline{2B}$ $\overline{3B}$ $\overline{3D}$ $\overline{3I}$

$\overline{3G}$ $\overline{3A}$ $\overline{3I}$ $\overline{2G}$ $\overline{1E}$

$\overline{2G}$ $\overline{2C}$ $\overline{2B}$

$\overline{2A}$ $\overline{3D}$ $\overline{3A}$ $\overline{1A}$ $\overline{2D}$ $\overline{3G}$ $\overline{3E}$ $\overline{1C}$ $\overline{2G}$ $\overline{2C}$?

$\overline{3G}$ $\overline{2C}$ $\overline{1E}$ $\overline{2B}$ $\overline{3E}$ $\overline{2B}$!

WHAT DO YOU GET WHEN YOU PUT
SOAPSUDS ON THE STOVE?

$\overline{3B}$ $\overline{1E}$ $\overline{3A}$ $\overline{3E}$ $\overline{1E}$ $\overline{2E}$

$\overline{2G}$ $\overline{2C}$ $\overline{2B}$

$\overline{3F}$ $\overline{3A}$ $\overline{2E}$ $\overline{3C}$ $\overline{2B}$.

WHAT HOLDS UP THE SUN?

$\overline{3G}$ $\overline{1G}$ $\overline{2E}$ $\overline{2A}$ $\overline{2B}$ $\overline{3A}$ $\overline{3E}$ $\overline{3G}$!

ON WHAT SIDE OF A HOUSE DOES A
TREE GROW BEST?

$\overline{1E}$ $\overline{2E}$ $\overline{2G}$ $\overline{2C}$ $\overline{2B}$

$\overline{1E}$ $\overline{1G}$ $\overline{2G}$ $\overline{3G}$ $\overline{1C}$ $\overline{1B}$ $\overline{2B}$

CODE CHART #25

real letter	A	B	C	D	E	F
code letter	F	M	O	L	R	P

real letter	G	H	I	J	K	L
code letter	E	N	A	G	Q	Z

real letter	M	N	O	P	Q	R
code letter	T	B	S	H	U	X

real letter	S	T	U	V	W	X
code letter	I	Y	W	C	V	K

real letter	Y	Z
code letter	D	J

IF I BOUGHT NEW WALLPAPER,
COULD I PUT IT ON MYSELF?

" A̅   Y̅N̅A̅B̅Q̅   A̅Y̅

V̅S̅W̅Z̅L̅   Z̅S̅S̅Q̅

M̅R̅Y̅Y̅R̅X̅   S̅B̅

Y̅N̅R̅   V̅F̅Z̅Z̅ !"

WHAT DO YOU GET WHEN YOU CROSS
A SKELETON WITH A DETECTIVE?

I̅N̅R̅X̅Z̅S̅O̅Q̅   M̅S̅B̅R̅I̅ !

"WHAT'S THE BEST REMEDY FOR
A POOR MEMORY?"

" A̅   O̅F̅B̅ Y̅

X̅R̅T̅R̅T̅M̅R̅X̅ !"

CODE CHART #1

```
A  B  C  D  E  F  G
10 21 16 30 35 24 18

H  I  J  K  L  M  N
27 32 12 34 22 14 13

O  P  Q  R  S  T  U
20 28 26 11 29 31 15

V  W  X  Y  Z
33 25 17 23 19
```

WHY ARE PIGS SUCH GREAT
SPORTS FANS?

B E C A U S E
21 35 16 10 15 29 35

T H E Y · R E
31 27 35 23   11 35

A L W A Y S
10 22 25 10 23 29

R O O T I N G !
11 20 20 31 32 13 18

"WHY DON'T YOU CONVINCE
YOUR BROTHER THAT HE'S
NOT A CHICKEN?"

· B E C A U S E
21 35 16 10 15 29 35

I   C A N
32   16 10 13

U S E   T H E
15 29 35   31 27 35

E G G S !·
35 18 18 29

M Y
14 23

D O G
30 20 18

N E V E R
13 35 33 35 11

B I T E S !
21 32 31 35 29

H O W
27 20 25

D O E S
30 20 35 29

I T
32 31

C H E W
16 27 35 25

I T S
32 31 29

F O O D ?
24 20 20 30

CODE CHART #2

real letter: A B C D E F G
code letter: LM DD HI RS ZZ YZ KL

real letter: H I J K L M N
code letter: ST NO UV PQ FG WX

real letter: O P Q R S T U
code letter: EE AA GH TU VW AZ BB

real letter: V W X Y Z
code letter: OP JK CC MN QR

THE (AZ ST ZZ)   TELL (AZ ZZ XY XY)

GARBAGE (KL LM TU DD LM KL ZZ)   HIM (ST NO FG) WE (JK ZZ)

MAN (FG LM WX) IS (NO VW)   DON'T (RS EE WX AZ)

HERE! (ST ZZ TU ZZ)   WANT (JK LM WX AZ)

ANY! (LM WX MN)

WHAT DOG KEEPS THE BEST TIME?

A (LM) WATCH (JK LM AZ HI ST)

DOG! (RS EE KL)

"WHAT'S THE CHANCE OF
BORROWING FIVE DOLLARS FROM YOU?"

"SLIM (VW XY NO FG) AND (LM WX RS)

NONE, (WX EE WX EE) AND (LM WX RS)

SLIM (VW XY NO FG) IS (NO VW)

OUT (EE BB AZ) OF (EE YZ)

TOWN!" (AZ EE JK WX)

WHY DO HAMBURGERS MAKE GOOD
BASEBALL PLAYERS?

THEY'RE (AZ ST ZZ MN · TU ZZ)

GREAT (KL TU ZZ LM AZ) AT (LM AZ)

THE (AZ ST ZZ) PLATE! (AA XY LM AZ ZZ)

CODE CHART #3

A B C D E F G H
+ ++ +++ -- -- -- ½ ½½

I J K L M N
½½½ ½ ½½ ½½½ = ==

O P Q R S T U V
=== +- -+ ½½ ½½ +½ ½+ -½

W X Y Z
½++ -½ ½- +-½

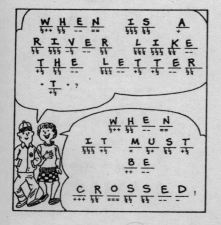

WHEN (½++ ½½ -- ==) IS (½½½ ½½) A (+)

RIVER (½½ ½½½ -½ ½½ ½½) LIKE (½½ ½½½ ½½ --)

THE (+½ ½½ --) LETTER (½½ ½½ +½ +½ ½½ ½½)

"T" (+½) ?

WHEN (½++ ½½ -- ==)

IT (½½½ +½) MUST (= ½+ ½½ +½)

BE (++ --)

CROSSED! (+++ ½½ === ½½ ½½ --)

"WHY DID YOU STOP TAKING SINGING
LESSONS?"

"MY (= ½-)

TEACHER (+½ -- + +++ ½½ -- ½½)

TOLD (+½ === ½½½ -)

ME (= ½½) I (½½½)

WAS (½++ + ½½)

THROWING (+½ ½½ ½½ ½½ === ½++ ½½½ == ½)

THE (+½ ½½ --)

PIANO (+- ½½½ + == ===)

OFF!" (=== --- ---)

WHAT QUESTION CAN NEVER BE
ANSWERED BY "YES"?

ARE (+ ½½ --) YOU (½- === ½+)

ASLEEP? (+ ½½ ½½½ -- -- +-)

CODE CHART #4

A=↑ N=⇍
B=↑↑ O=⇚
C=↑↑↑ P=↑↓
D=↓ Q=↓↑↓
E=↓↓ R=⇄
F=↓↓↓ S=⇋
G=↕ T=↑↓↑
H=↕↕ U=↓↑↓
I=↕↕↕ V=→↑
J=→ W=↑→
K=⇉ X=↓←
L=⇇ Y=←↓
M=← Z=↓↑

WHY DID THE INDIAN STAND IN FRONT OF THE MOTEL?

BECAUSE HE DIDN'T HAVE A RESERVATION.

WHAT WAS THE RABBIT DOING IN FRONT OF THE CANDLE?

MAKING SHADOWS OF PEOPLE.

"ARE YOU AFRAID OF HEIGHTS?"

NO. I'M AFRAID OF WIDTHS."

WHY DO WE BUY CLOTHES?

BECAUSE WE CAN'T GET THEM FOR NOTHING!

CODE CHART #5

	A	B	C	D	E	F	G
A	D	E	L	M	T	U	Y
B	C	F	K	N	S	V	Z
C	B	G	J	O	R	W	
D	A	H	I	P	Q	X	

WHAT DID ONE SCARECROW SAY TO THE OTHER SCARECROW?

"HAY, MAN!"

WHAT KIND OF SHOES ARE MADE OUT OF BANANA SKINS?

SLIPPERS!

WHAT MOST RESEMBLES HALF A CHEESE?

THE OTHER HALF!

WHAT BECOMES HIGHER WHEN THE HEAD IS OFF?

A PILLOW!

WHAT ROOM CAN NO ONE ENTER?

A MUSHROOM!

CODE CHART #6

A=⊙ N=□
B=⊟ O=□□
C=● P=○
D=⊙⊙ Q=○○
E=⊡⊡ R=□○
F=●● S=○□
G=⊙□ T=□○□
H=□⊙ U=○□○
I=⊙□⊙ V=□⊟
J=□⊙□ W=⊟□
K=■■ X=○⊙
L=□● Y=○⊙
M=●□ Z=⊙□⊙

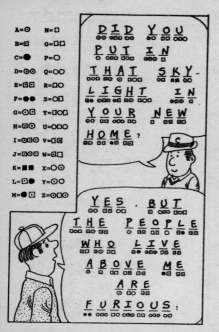

DID YOU PUT IN THAT SKY-LIGHT IN YOUR NEW HOME?

YES, BUT THE PEOPLE WHO LIVE ABOVE ME ARE FURIOUS!

WHAT KIND OF BRICK IS SOFT?

F A B R I C ?

WHY CAN'T YOU TRUST BANK CLERKS WITH SECRETS?

BECAUSE THEY'RE TELLERS!

WHAT DO YOU ALWAYS FIND IN YOUR POCKET WHEN YOU REACH IN?

YOUR HAND

CODE CHART #7

A= 275 N= 175
B= 475 O= 425
C= 125 P= 350
D= 525 Q= 250
E= 725 R= 625
F= 325 S= 100
G= 500 T= 550
H= 675 U= 450
I= 225 V= 700
J= 650 W= 300
K= 600 X= 575
L= 150 Y= 375
M= 400 Z= 200

HOW
675 425 300

WOULD
300 425 450 150 525

YOU
375 425 450

GREET
500 625 725 725 550

SMOKEY
100 400 425 600 725 375

THE
550 675 725

BEAR?
475 725 275 625

WITH A
300 225 550 675   275

BEAR HUG!
475 725 275 625   675 450 500

WHAT GOOD IS HAVING A MICROWAVE FIREPLACE?

YOU CAN
375 425 450   125 275 175

SPEND
100 350 725 175 525

AN
275 175

EVENING
725 700 725 175 225 175 500

IN
225 175

FRONT
325 625 425 175 550

OF THE
425 325   550 675 725

FIRE IN
325 225 625 725   225 175

UNDER
450 175 525 725 625

EIGHT
725 225 500 675 550

MINUTES!
400 225 175 450 550 725 100

CODE CHART #8

real letter	A	B	C	D	E	F	G	H	I	J	K	L	M
code letter	J	F	L	G	N	P	R	T	W	A	Q	Y	U

real letter	N	O	P	Q	R	S	T	U	V	W	X	Y	Z
code letter	B	V	H	C	M	X	I	D	O	S	E	Z	K

DO YOU ENJOY
G V   Z V D   N B A V Z

YOUR JOB
Z V D H   A V F

CLEANING
L Y N J B W B R

CHIMNEYS?
L T W U B N Z X

YES, I THINK
Z N X   W   I T W B Q

IT SOOTS
W I   X V V I X

ME.
U N

"DO YOU THINK WE OUGHT TO HAVE BUTTERFLY CHAIRS?"

NO! LET THEM
B V   Y N I   I T N U

FLY AROUND!
P Y Z   J M V D B G

WHAT DO THEY DO WITH THE LEFTOVER HOLES IN DOUGHNUTS?

THEY TIE THEM
I T N Z   I W N   I T N U

UP WITH
D H   S W I T

STRING AND
X I M W B R   J B G

MAKE FISH
U J Q N   P W X T

NETS!
B N I X

"YOU HAVE YOUR SHOES ON THE WRONG FEET!"

"THEY'RE THE
I T N Z   M N   I T N

ONLY FEET
V B Y Z   P N N I

I HAVE!"
W   T J O N

CODE CHART #9

	1	2	3	4	5	6	7
■	V	W	X	Y	Z		
▲	O	P	Q	R	S	T	U
✶	H	I	J	K	L	M	N
●	A	B	C	D	E	F	G

WHEN IS
■2 ▲1 •5 ✶7   ▲2 ▲5

A ROPE
•1   ▲4 ▲1 •2 •5

LIKE A
✶5 ✶2 ▲4 •5   •1

STICK OF
▲5 ✶2 ✶3 •3 ✶4   ▲4 •6

WOOD?
■2 ▲1 ▲1 •4

WHEN IT
■2 ▲1 •5 ✶7   ▲2 ▲6

HAS KNOTS!
✶1 •1 ▲5   ✶4 ✶7 ▲1 ▲6 ▲5

"WHERE'S YOUR DOG?"

I SPILLED
✶2   ▲5 ▲2 ✶2 ▲5 ▲5 •5 •4

SPOT
▲5 ▲5 •2 ▲6

REMOVER ON
▲4 •5 ✶6 ▲1 •1 •5 ▲4   ▲1 ✶7

HIM AND
✶1 ✶2 ✶6   •1 ✶7 •4

NOW HE'S
✶7 ▲1 ■2   ✶1 •5 ▲5

GONE!"
•7 ▲1 ✶7 •5

"MY NAME IS JOE, WHAT CAN I CALL YOU?"

ANYTHING
•1 ✶7 ■4 ▲6 ✶1 ▲2 ✶7 •7

YOU WANT.
■4 ▲1 ▲7   ■2 •1 ✶7 ▲6

JUST
✶3 ▲7 ▲5 ▲6

DON'T CALL
•4 ▲1 ✶7 ▲6   •3 •1 ✶5 ✶5

ME LATE
✶6 •5   ✶5 •1 ▲6 •5

FOR
•6 ▲1 ▲4

DINNER!"
•4 ✶2 ✶7 ✶7 •5 ▲4

CODE CHART #10

A= •	N= •|•
B= ••	O= •—•
C= •••	P= |•|
D= |	Q= —•—
E= ||	R= •|••
F= |||	S= ••|•
G= —	T= |•|
H= ==	U= •|—
I= ≡	V= —||
J= •|	W= =|
K= •—•	X= ||—
L= |•|	Y= —||
M= —•	Z= ||=

"IF YOU SHOVELED SNOW FOR 25
PEOPLE AND THEY EACH PAID
YOU FOUR DOLLARS, WHAT
WOULD YOU GET?"

· A   NEW
BICYCLE !·

"IS THIS THE END OF THE LINE?"

·NO   IT·S
THE
BEGINNING
AND WE·RE
ALL
FACING
BACKWARDS·!·

CODE CHART #11

SUN	MON	TUE	WED	THU	FRI	SAT
	¹ L	² N	³ H	⁴ B	⁵ Q	⁶ K
⁷ F	⁸ R	⁹ C	¹⁰ V	¹¹ P	¹² Z	¹³ E
¹⁴ A	¹⁵ M	¹⁶ U	¹⁷ G	¹⁸ W	¹⁹ J	²⁰ X
²¹ I	²² T	²³ O	²⁴ Y	²⁵ S	²⁶ D	

WHAT   IS
THU WED SUN MON   SUN THU
18   3   14 22   21   25

A   BULL
SUN   THU TUE MON MON
14   4   16 1   1

CALLED
TUE SUN MON MON SAT FRI
9   14 1   1   13 26

WHEN
THU WED SUN TUE
18 3   13 2

HE·S
WED SAT   THU
3   13   25

SLEEPING ?
THU MON SAT SAT THU SUN TUE WED
25 1   13 13 11 21 2   17

A
SUN
14

BULLDOZER !
THU TUE MON MON FRI TUE FRI SAT MON
4   16 1   1   26 2   12 13 8

WHAT GOES UP INTO THE AIR
WHITE AND COMES DOWN YELLOW
AND WHITE?

AN   EGG !
SUN TUE   SAT WED WED
14 2   13 17 17

WHAT DO YOU GET WHEN YOU
CROSS A KANGAROO WITH A
747 JET?

A   PLANE
SUN   THU MON SUN TUE SAT
14   22 1   14 2   13

THAT
MON WED SUN MON
22 3   14 22

MAKES
MON SUN SAT SAT THU
15 14 6   13 25

SHORT
THU WED TUE MON MON
25 3   23 8   22

HOPS !
WED TUE THU THU
3   23 11 25

CODE CHART #12

✱	■	▲	●
1 Q	1 E	1 S	1 I
2 H	2 P	2 R	2 X
3 Y	3 L	3 B	3 O
4 M	4 G	4 T	4 D
5 C	5 U	5 F	5 W
6 J	6 K	6 N	6 Z
	7 A	7 V	

HOW DO YOU MAKE NOTES
OF STONE?

JUST REARRANGE
6 5 1 4   2 1 7 2 2 7 6 4 1

THE LETTERS!
4 2 1   3 1 4 4 1 2 1

HOW CAN YOU TELL IF THIS IS
A DOGWOOD TREE?

BY ITS BARK!
3 3   1 4 1   3 7 2 6

"HOW DO YOU LIKE SCHOOL?"

"CLOSED!"
5 3 3 1 1 4

CODE CHART #13

	10	20	30	40	50	60	70
a	D	E	L	N	T	U	Y
b	C	F	K	N	S	V	Z
c	B	G	J	O	R	W	
d	A	H	I	P	Q	X	

HOW DO YOU MAKE SOUP GOLD?

PUT IN
40 60 50   30 40
d a a   d b

FOURTEEN
20 40 60 50 50 20 20 40
b c a c a a a b

CARROTS!
10 10 50 50 40 40 50 50
b d c c c a b

WHAT'S PURPLE AND FLIES?

SUPERGRAPE!
50 60 40 20 50 20 50 10 40 20
b a d a c c c d d a

WHAT'S HIGHER THAN A
BUILDING AND SEEMS SMALLER
THAN A FROG?

A STAR!
10   50 50 10 50
d   b a d c

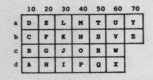

CODE CHART #14

"DID YOU HEAR THE STORY ABOUT THE MOUNTAIN?"

YES, IT'S
ALL A
BLUFF!"

WHAT DO
YOU CALL
A SILLY
SNOWMAN?

A
SNOWFLAKE!

WHAT DOES A VAMPIRE DO WHEN HE GETS TIRED OF WORKING?

HE TAKES
A COFFIN
BREAK!

WHAT KIND OF SANDWICHES DO SAILORS LIKE?

SUBMARINE
SANDWICHES!

CODE CHART #15

A	B	C	D	E	F	G
12	5	24	18	8	16	21

H	I	J	K	L	M	N
2	14	26	11	20	6	4

O	P	Q	R	S
17	9	1	13	7

T	U	V	W	X	Y	Z
23	19	10	22	15	3	25

WHAT
22 2 12 23

COUNTRY IS
24 17 19 4 23 13 3   14 7

GOOD FOR
21 17 17 18   16 17 13

SKATERS?
7 11 12 23 8 13 7

ICELAND!
14 24 8 20 12 4 18

WHAT DO YOU CALL A GIANT BELL THAT'S COVERED WITH HAIR?

KING GONG!
11 14 4 21   21 17 4 21

WHERE'S A GOOD PLACE TO GO WHEN YOU'RE BROKE?

TO WORK!
23 17   22 17 13 11

WHAT PEN SHOULD NEVER BE USED FOR WRITING?

A PIG PEN!
12   9 14 21   9 8 4

CODE CHART #16

real letter	A	B	C	D	E	F	G
code letter	L	H	Q	V	Z	D	N

real letter	H	I	J	K	L	M	N
code letter	S	E	P	A	R	I	Y

real letter	O	P	Q	R	S	T	U
code letter	M	B	J	U	G	O	X

real letter	V	W	X	Y	Z
code letter	F	T	K	W	C

WHAT COMES WITH AN AIRPLANE,
GOES WITH AN AIRPLANE AND IS
NO USE TO AN AIRPLANE?

NOISE!
Y M E G Z

WHO GETS PAID FOR NEVER DOING
A DAY'S WORK?

A NIGHT
L   Y E N S O

WATCHMAN.
T L O Q S I L Y

WHAT GOES UP AND NEVER
GOES DOWN?

YOUR AGE.
W M X U   L N Z

WHEN DOES ROAST
T S Z Y   V M Z G   U M L G O

BEEF COST
H Z Z D   Q M G O

THE MOST?
O S Z   I N G O

WHEN IT'S
T S Z Y   E O G

RARE!
U L U Z

CODE CHART #17

A	B	C	D	E	F
35	85	20	90	105	50

G	H	I	J	K	L
45	70	115	5	110	10

M	N	O	P	Q	R
60	100	80	30	75	95

S	T	U	V
25	120	55	125

W	X	Y	Z
40	15	65	130

WHERE'S
40 70 105 95 105   25

A GOOD
35   45 80 80 90

PLACE FOR A
30 10 35 20 105   50 80 95   35

GIANT APE
45 115 35 100 120   35 30 105

TO SIT?
120 80   25 115 120

ANYWHERE
35 100 65 40 70 105 95 105

IT WANTS TO!
115 120   40 35 100 120 25   120 80

WHY DOES TARZAN SWING THROUGH
THE TREES?

SO HE
25 80   70 105

WON'T GET
40 80 100 120   45 105 120

HIS
70 115 25

SHOES
25 70 80 105 25

DIRTY!
90 115 95 120 65

HOW CAN YOU TELL IF AN ELEPHANT
HAS BEEN IN YOUR KITCHEN?

BY THE
85 65   120 70 105

PEANUT
30 105 35 100 55 120

SHELLS
25 70 105 10 10 25

IN THE
115 100   120 70 105

SINK!
25 115 100 110

CODE CHART #18

A	B	C	D	E	F	G
G	K	S	A	Z	J	R

H	I	J	K	L	M	N
D	V	F	M	T	U	B

O	P	Q	R	S	T	U
N	O	W	E	L	C	X

V	W	X	Y	Z		
Q	H	Y	P	I		

"DO YOU REALLY HAVE BAD LUCK?"

IF IT STARTED
V̲J̲ V̲C̲ L̲C̲G̲E̲C̲Z̲A̲

RAINING SOUP,
E̲G̲V̲B̲V̲B̲R̲ L̲N̲X̲O̲

I·D BE
V̲ A̲ K̲Z̲

STANDING THERE
L̲C̲G̲B̲A̲V̲B̲R̲ C̲D̲Z̲E̲Z̲

WITH
H̲V̲C̲D̲

A FORK!"
G̲ J̲N̲E̲M̲

NAME A LIQUID THAT CAN'T FREEZE.

HOT WATER!
D̲N̲C̲ H̲G̲C̲Z̲E̲

WHAT TWO
H̲D̲G̲C̲ C̲H̲N̲

ANIMALS GO
G̲B̲V̲U̲G̲T̲L̲ R̲N̲

WITH YOU
H̲V̲C̲D̲ P̲N̲X̲

EVERYWHERE?
Z̲Q̲Z̲E̲P̲H̲D̲Z̲E̲Z̲

YOUR CALVES!
P̲N̲X̲E̲ S̲G̲T̲Q̲Z̲L̲

CODE CHART #19

A	B	C	D	E	F	G
12	1	13	4	15	9	14

H	I	J	K	L		
7	3	19	11	17		

M	N	O	P	Q	R	S
6	10	5	21	8	22	24

T	U	V	W	X	Y	Z
20	2	26	18	25	23	16

"WHY DO THEY CALL YOUR
BROTHER CHOCOLATE BAR?"

·BECAUSE
1 15 13 12 2 24 15

HE·S
7 15 24

HALF NUTS!"
7 12 17 9 10 2 20 24

WHERE WERE THE FIRST
DOUGHNUTS FRIED?

IN GREECE!
3 10 14 22 15 15 13 15

IF APRIL SHOWERS BRING MAY
FLOWERS, WHAT DO MAY FLOWERS
BRING?

PILGRIMS!
21 3 17 14 22 3 6 24

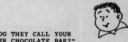

WHAT·S
18 7 12 20 24

PURPLE AND
21 2 22 21 17 15 12 10 4

GLOWS?
14 17 5 18 24

AN
12 10

ELECTRIC
15 17 15 13 20 22 3 13

GRAPE!
14 22 12 21 15

CODE CHART #20

A= 7 N= 4
B= 14 O= 13
C= 1 P= 18
D= 22 Q= 10
E= 8 R= 19
F= 15 S= 3
G= 23 T= 20
H= 9 U= 24
I= 16 V= 26
J= 2 W= 11
K= 17 X= 25
L= 6 Y= 21
M= 12 Z= 5

W H A T
11 9 7 20

T I M E
20 16 12 8

S P E L L E D
3 18 8 6 6 8 22

B A C K W A R D
14 7 1 17 11 7 19 22

A N D
7 4 22

F O R W A R D
15 13 19 11 7 19 22

I S   T H E
16 3   20 9 8

S A M E ?
3 7 12 8

N O O N !
4 13 13 4

WHAT TRAVELS ABOUT AND WEARS
OUT SHOES, BUT HAS NO SHOES TO
WEAR?

A   F O O T B A L L !
7   15 13 13 20 14 7 6 6

"IF I HAD TWO HOTDOGS AND YOU
HAD TWO HOTDOGS, WHAT WOULD WE
HAVE?

- L U N C H !"
6 24 4 1 9

"DID YOU HEAR THE JOKE ABOUT
THE BOY WHO POPPED THE
POTATO CHIP BAG?"

- Y E S , I T
21 8 3   16 20

W A S   C R U M B Y !"
11 7 3   1 19 24 12 14 21

CODE CHART #21

A	B	C	D	E	F
+6	4	+7	3	+1	+8
G	H	I	J	K	L
5-	+2	-3	+9	-2	6
M	N	O	P	Q	R
+3	-4	-1	2	+4	-6
S	T	U	V	W	X
7	+5	1	-5	8	-7
		Y	Z		
		9	-8		

W H A T   M A K E S
8 +2 +6 +5   +3 +6 -2 +1 7

A   P A I R
+6   2 +6 -3 -6

O F
-1 +8

S N E A K E R S ?
7 -4 +1 +6 -2 +1 -6 7

T W O
+5 8 -1

S N E A K E R S !
7 -4 +1 +6 -2 +1 -6 7

WHEN IS THE WORST WEATHER FOR
RATS AND MICE?

W H E N   I T
8 -4 +1 -4   -3 +5

R A I N S   C A T S
-6 +6 -3 -4 7   +7 +6 +5 7

A N D   D O G S !
+6 -4 3   3 -1 5 7

WHAT MAKES A ROAD BROAD?

T H E   L E T T E R
+5 +2 +1   6 +1 +5 +5 +1 -6

- B " !
4

"IF A LION WERE STALKING YOU,
WHAT STEPS WOULD YOU TAKE?"

- T H E
+5 +2 +1

L O N G E S T
6 -1 -4 5 +1 7 +5

S T E P S   I
7 +5 +1 2 7   -3

C O U L D !-
+7 -1 1 6 3

CODE CHART #22

A	B	C	D	E	F
5	11	1	10	25	6
	G	H	I	J	
	12	2	24	23	
K	L	M	N	O	P
26	2	13	20	4	21
	Q	R	S	T	
	14	18	7	19	
U	V	W	X	Y	Z
8	15	3	16	9	17

DOES YOUR
10 4 25 7   9 4 8 18
WATCH
3 5 19 1 22
TELL TIME?
19 25 2 2   19 24 13 25

NO, YOU
20 4   9 4 8
HAVE TO
22 5 15 25   19 4
LOOK AT
2 4 4 26   5 19
IT!
24 19

WHAT IS THE NAME OF THE
FEATHERS THAT GROW
ON A CHICKEN'S WING?

CHICKEN
1 22 24 1 26 25 20
FEATHERS!
6 25 5 19 22 25 18 7

HENRY THE BUTCHER IS SIX FEET
TALL AND HAS BROWN HAIR.
WHAT DOES HE WEIGH?

MEAT!
13 25 5 19

"IF I HAD A SLICE OF PIZZA
AND YOU HAD ONLY A BITE, WHAT
WOULD YOU DO?"

"SCRATCH
7 1 18 5 19 1 22
IT!"
24 19

CODE CHART #23

A= 8B	N= 1D
B= 5D	O= 5E
C= 1B	P= 4B
D= 6E	Q= 2H
E= 4H	R= 6M
F= 7I	S= 5C
G= 2B	T= 7F
H= 9C	U= 3D
I= 8D	V= 2J
J= 2G	W= 6B
K= 3B	X= 3K
L= 9N	Y= 1G
M= 1D	Z= 7C

WHAT
6B 9C 8B 7F
DO
6E 5E
YOU
1G 5E 3D
CALL
1B 8B 9N 9N
A
8B
DANCING
6E 8B 1D 1B 8D 1D 2B
STEER?
5C 7F 4H 4H 6M

BULLERINA!
5D 3D 9N 9N 4H 6M 8D 1D 8B

WHAT DID THE PENCIL SAY TO THE
PAPER?

"I DOT MY
8D   6E 5E 7F   1D 1G
EYES ON
4H 1G 4H 5C   5E 1D
YOU!"
1G 5E 3D

"DOES THE WATER ALWAYS COME
THROUGH THE ROOF OF YOUR CAR?"

"ONLY WHEN
5E 1D 9N 1G   6B 9C 4H 1D
IT RAINS!"
8D 7F   6M 8B 8D 1D 5C

WHAT DID ONE POTATO CHIP SAY
TO THE OTHER?

"LET'S GO
9N 4H 7F 5C   2B 5E
FOR
7I 5E 6M
A DIP."
8B   6E 8D 4B

CODE CHART #24

	A	B	C	D	E	F	G	H	I
1	C	D	I	J	O	P	U	V	
2	B	E	H	K	N	Q	T	W	Z
3	A	F	G	L	M	R	S	X	Y

WHAT DO YOU GET WHEN YOU PUT
SOAPSUDS ON THE STOVE?

F O A M   O N
3B 1E 3A 3E   1E 2E

T H E
2G 2C 2B

R A N G E .
3F 3A 2E 3C 2B

WHAT HOLDS UP THE SUN?

S U N B E A M S !
3G 1G 2E 2A 2B 3A 3E 3G

ON WHAT SIDE OF A HOUSE DOES A
TREE GROW BEST?

O N   T H E
1E 2E   2G 2C 2B

O U T S I D E .
1E 1G 2G 3G 1C 1B 2B

W H A T   D I D
2H 2C 3A 2G   1B 1C 1B

T H E
2G 2C 2B

H O R S E F L Y
2C 1E 3F 3G 2B 3B 3B 3I

S A Y   T O
3G 3A 3I   2G 1E

T H E
2G 2C 2B

B L A C K S M I T H ?
2A 3D 3A 1A 2D 3G 3E 1C 2G 2C

S H O E   M E !
3G 2C 1E 2B   3E 2B

CODE CHART #25

real letter	A	B	C	D	E	F
code letter	F	M	O	L	R	P

real letter	G	H	I	J	K	L
code letter	E	N	A	G	Q	Z

real letter	M	N	O	P	Q	R
code letter	T	B	S	H	U	X

real letter	S	T	U	V	W	X
code letter	I	Y	W	C	V	K

real letter	Y	Z
code letter	D	J

IF I BOUGHT NEW WALLPAPER,
COULD I PUT IT ON MYSELF?

· I   T H I N K   I T
  A   Y N A B Q   A Y

W O U L D   L O O K
V S W Z L   Z S S Q

B E T T E R   O N
M R Y Y R X   S B

T H E   W A L L !·
Y N R   V F Z Z

WHAT DO YOU GET WHEN YOU CROSS
A SKELETON WITH A DETECTIVE?

S H E R L O C K   B O N E S !
I N R X Z S O Q   M S B R I

"WHAT'S THE BEST REMEDY FOR
A POOR MEMORY?"

· I   C A N · T
  A   O F B   Y

R E M E M B E R !·
X R T R T M R X

HOW DO ANGELS
NSV LS FBERZI

GREET EACH
EXRRY RFON

OTHER ?
SYNRX

THEY SAY
YNRD IFD

·HALO·!
NFZS